*For William Nicolas*

MYRIAD BOOKS LIMITED
35 Bishopsthorpe Road, London SE26 4PA

First published in 1996 by
FRANCES LINCOLN LIMITED
4 Torriano Mews, Torriano Avenue
London NW5 2RZ

ISBN 1 84746 005 4

EAN 9 781 84746 005 9

Printed in China

# Bumper to Bumper

## A Traffic Jam
## by Jakki Wood

MYRIAD BOOKS LIMITED

hatchback car

cement mixer                    bicycle

delivery van                    caravan

four-wheel-drive car

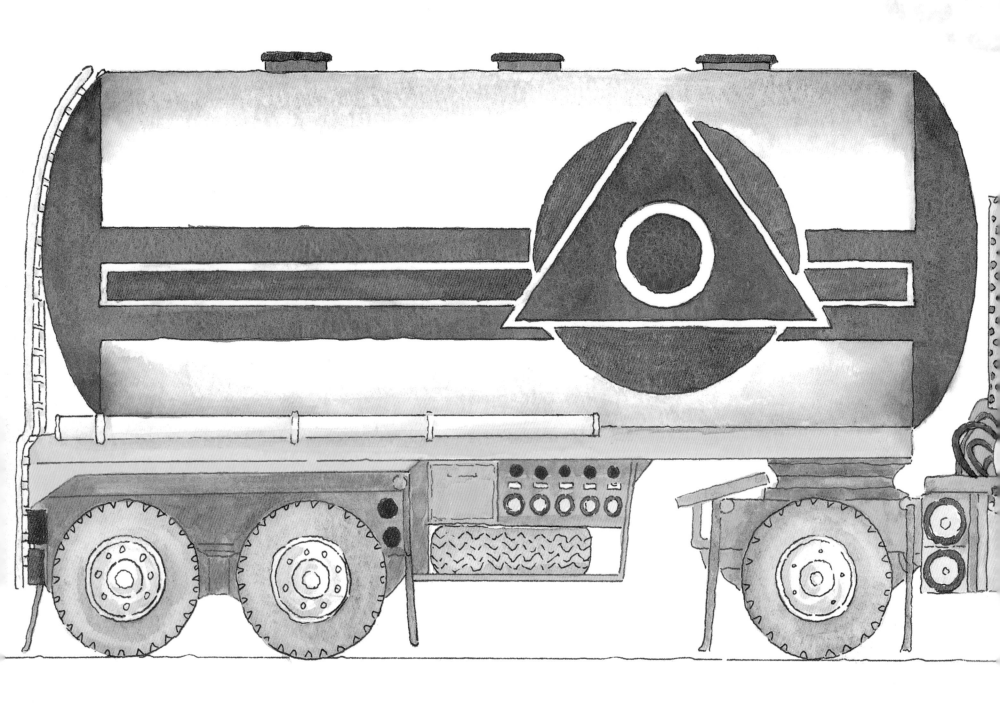

petrol tanker

flatbed lorry

estate car

horsebox

jeep

parcel van

sports car

boat                    convertible

eighteen-wheeler

lorry

old car                    bus stop

bus

four-door saloon

pick-up truck                    motorbike

plough and tractor

vintage car                    roadworks

drill                    lorry cab

dumper truck

road roller                                    tandem

broken-down car                    breakdown truck

refuse lorry

people carrier

children crossing!